What *Jazz 'n' Blues* Can I P
Violin
Grades One, Two & Three

Series Editors: Mark Mumford and Tim Siddall

Music arranged and processed by
Barnes Music Engraving Ltd
East Sussex TN22 4HA, England

Published 1996

© International Music Publications Limited
Southend Road, Woodford Green, Essex IG8 8HN, England

Reproducing this music in any form is illegal and forbidden
by the Copyright, Designs and Patents Act 1988

Introduction

In this *What Jazz 'n' Blues Can I Play?* collection you'll find twelve popular tunes that are both challenging and entertaining.

The pieces have been carefully selected and arranged to provide a fascinating introduction to jazz and blues, and are ideal for young violinists who are either working towards or have recently taken a Grade One, Two or Three violin examination.

Technical demands increase progressively, gradually introducing new concepts, and each piece offers suggestions and guidelines on bowing, fingering, dynamics and tempo, together with technical tips and performance notes.

Whether it's for light relief from examination preparation, or to reinforce the understanding of new concepts, this collection will enthuse and encourage all young violin players.

When the Saints go marching in

Traditional

© 1996 International Music Publications Limited, Woodford Green, Essex IG8 8HN

Jeepers creepers

Words by Johnny Mercer, Music by Harry Warren

© 1938 & 1996 M Witmark & Sons, USA

B Feldman & Co Ltd, London WC2H 0EA

U.F.O. blues

Words by Tom Stanier, Music by Jim Parker

© 1986 & 1996 International Music Publications Limited, Woodford Green, Essex IG8 8HN

Pennsylvania 6-5000

By Carl Sigman and Jerry Gray

© 1940 & 1996 EMI Catalogue Partnership and EMI Robbins Catalog Inc, USA
Worldwide print controlled by Warner Bros Publications Inc/IMP Ltd

Little brown jug

Traditional

© 1996 International Music Publications Limited, Woodford Green, Essex IG8 8HN

Sentimental journey

Words and Music by Bud Green, Les Brown and Ben Homer

© 1944 & 1996 Morley Music Co, USA
Warner/Chappell Music Ltd, London W1Y 3FA

Basin St. Blues

Words and Music by Spencer Williams

© 1929 & 1996 Triangle Music Co Inc, USA
EMI Music Publishing Ltd, London WC2H 0EA

Black bottom

Words by Lew Brown and Buddy De-Sylva, Music by Ray Henderson

© 1927 & 1996 Harms Inc, USA
Redwood Music Ltd, London NW1 8BD

What Jazz 'n' Blues Can I Play?
Violin
Grades One, Two & Three

When the Saints go marching in

Traditional

This 'trad.' jazz standard has its origins in gospel music. 'Trad.' style is that associated with the traditional jazz roots of New Orleans. Amongst the hundreds of famous versions are recordings by Fats Domino, Elvis Presley and Louis Armstrong. You might hear the song (or something like it!) chanted by the supporters of Southampton Football Club, and it also was chosen as the marching tune for the American team in the opening ceremony of the 1996 Olympic Games in Atlanta, USA.

This piece can withstand a really lively performance, be bold! To achieve a strong, energetic sound use full, heavy bows close to the bridge. There's a lot of G major arpeggio in the melody; listen to your tuning and in particular be sure to use the tip of your third finger, so the sound is really clear. Count the tied notes carefully, you don't want to get out of step when people start dancing!

© 1996 International Music Publications Limited, Woodford Green, Essex IG8 8HN

Jeepers creepers

Words by Johnny Mercer, Music by Harry Warren

With bounce (♩ = 132)

This song is from the musical film *Going Places*, in which jazz great Louis Armstrong sings to a horse, whose name is Jeepers Creepers. Johnny Mercer and Harry Warren also wrote 'You Must Have Been A Beautiful Baby'. Both had long and successful careers as songwriters, each working with a variety of other writers. Warren's teamwork with Al Dubin, writing for the movie industry, produced 'We're In The Money', 'I Only Have Eyes For You' and 'Lullaby Of Broadway'. Johnny Mercer co-wrote with Jerome Kern and Henry Mancini, amongst others. He also was a co-founder of Capitol Records.

Give your performance lots of energy and don't be afraid to use plenty of bow for the longer notes. Try to vary your bowing style, it works well to play the longer notes smoothly, *legato*, and the crotchets and quavers more separated, or *staccato*. Notice how the tune is made up of four bar phrases which repeat, with slight variation. Interest can be built up in the dynamic contrasts; experiment with this if you like but do make the contrasts clear. Keep your fourth finger prepared and watch out for the G sharp in bar 15!

© 1938 & 1996 M Witmark & Sons, USA
B Feldman & Co Ltd, London WC2H 0EA

U.F.O. blues

Words by Tom Stanier, Music by Jim Parker

Spookily (♩ = 112)

This tune is from the children's musical play *Blast Off!*. Jim Parker has written several shows with Tom Stanier, whom he met while they both were working at the BBC. He also composed music for the TV productions of *House Of Cards*, *House Of Eliott* and *Soldier Soldier* and wrote incidental music for the radio station Jazz FM.

Take the character of this piece from the performance style marking, 'Spookily'. Enjoy swinging the quavers with a spiky mysterious feel. The ending sounds really dramatic and scary if you start the *crescendo* very quietly, getting louder through each bar and then come in really positively after the minim rest.

© 1986 & 1996 International Music Publications Limited, Woodford Green, Essex IG8 8HN

Pennsylvania 6-5000

By Carl Sigman and Jerry Gray

Jerry Gray (1915–1976) earned an early reputation as a jazz accordionist but then went on to concentrate on composing and arranging. After a spell with Artie Shaw, for whom he arranged 'Begin The Beguine', he worked with Glenn Miller. 'Pennsylvania 6-5000' and 'A String Of Pearls' are two of his best known contributions to the Miller band repertoire. Gray continued to work with Miller during military service, with the Army Air Force Orchestra, taking over as leader after Miller's death in 1944.

Swing the quavers in this piece in an unhurried way and experiment with shortening the crotchets a little, for instance in bars 2, 4, and 6; this should create a lighter feel. You can use some crescendo for expressive effect within phrases, particularly toward accented notes and through repeated quavers. Finally, you're invited to improvise a flourish over the last chord, which is marked 'ad lib'.

© 1940 & 1996 EMI Catalogue Partnership and EMI Robbins Catalog Inc, USA
Worldwide print controlled by Warner Bros Publications Inc/IMP Ltd

Little brown jug

Traditional

This song was made popular by the Weatherwax Brothers Quartet in 1911, and was revived by Glenn Miller and his orchestra in 1939 in an arrangement by Bill Finegan; a recording of which became Miller's first million seller. Joseph Eastburn Winner (1837–1918) was the brother of Septimus Winner (1827–1902) who wrote 'Listen To The Mocking Bird' and 'Oh Where, Oh Where Has My Little Dog Gone?'.

The first time round this tune should be simple and straightforward, without any swing. When the tune returns as a variation, at bar 10, use sudden surges of bow speed to make accents and bring out the syncopated rhythm. In bar 13 practise separate bows first, then introduce the jazzy rhythm and finally add the slur and accent on the E flat. Try to be as free as possible with the rhythm, without losing the beat, and give the piece a strong finish.

© 1996 International Music Publications Limited, Woodford Green, Essex IG8 8HN

Sentimental journey

Words and Music by Bud Green, Les Brown and Ben Homer

In the year of its release, 1945, this song went to No.1 in the USA's Billboard chart. It became known as the theme song of Les Brown and his orchestra (composer Ben Homer was the band's arranger) but was also covered by numerous others, including Frank Sinatra and Ella Fitzgerald. Les Brown worked for many years with comedian Bob Hope.

Try to feel a steady, laid-back crotchet pulse as you're playing and make those late entries, after each quaver rest, sound easy. If you can play in third position you'll find that staying on the D string helps maintain a rich, warm sound, which will be warmer still if you add some vibrato on the long notes.

© 1944 & 1996 Morley Music Co, USA

Warner/Chappell Music Ltd, London W1Y 3FA

Basin St. Blues

Words and Music by Spencer Williams

This tune is a 'trad.' jazz standard which has been played by all the greats; Louis Armstrong and Glenn Miller to name but two. Spencer Williams was actually born on Basin Street, in New Orleans, in 1889. His varied career included a stint as a pianist in an amusement arcade. He also worked in Paris, where he composed for the artistic dancer Josephine Baker in her performances at the *Folies Bergère*.

The syncopated, jazzy rhythm in this piece is very repetitive; give it a swing by moving the bow freely and spring off the first beat of each bar. In bars 9, 10 and 16 the slurs go over each beat, which should produce a lazy feel. For practise, try these with separate bows at first so you avoid getting tangled up.

© 1929 & 1996 Triangle Music Co Inc, USA
EMI Music Publishing Ltd, London WC2H 0EA

Black bottom

Words by Lew Brown and Buddy De-Sylva, Music by Ray Henderson

The writing partnership of Buddy DeSylva, Lew Brown and Ray Henderson enjoyed a long association which included running their own publishing company in New York. This is one of the songs they created for the spectacular revue *George White's Scandals* (1926) which starred Ann Pennington. It became known as Pennington's theme song and made *The Black Bottom* dance, which the song describes, famous. Amongst numerous other hits written by the same team were 'The Best Things In Life Are Free', 'You're The Cream In My Coffee', 'Sonny Boy' and 'Button Up Your Overcoat'.

Feeling the beat as two in a bar helps sustain the energy without the piece sounding too chopped up. Move through repeated notes, like the crotchets in bars 9 and 17, in a way that doesn't sound dull. One method of adding expression to a phrase is to use a slight crescendo and choose certain notes to 'lean' on a little bit more than their neighbours. The middle section works best played in third position. Try for a percussive sound in bars 24 and 28.

© 1927 & 1996 Harms Inc, USA

Redwood Music Ltd, London NW1 8BD

Blue moon

Words by Lorenz Hart, Music by Richard Rodgers

This classic ballad has been arranged in many different ways, fast and slow, from Rosemary Clooney to Sha Na Na. The writing partnership of Rodgers and Hart lasted more than twenty years and produced numerous stage musicals and film scores, full of great songs. In 1982 further manuscripts of theirs were discovered amongst the contents of storage crates in a Warner Bros. warehouse.

To give this piece a dreamy atmosphere play legato, slow and sustained, with a lazy feel to the shorter notes. You could add some vibrato for more expression and you might choose certain moments to 'slide' into a note. This has to be done gracefully if it is to sound like anything other than a mistake, so it is best practised in private to begin with!

© 1934 & 1996 EMI Catalogue Partnership and EMI Robbins Catalog Inc, USA
Worldwide print rights controlled by Warner Bros Publications Inc/IMP Ltd

Five foot two, eyes of blue
(Has anybody seen my girl?)

Words by Joe Young and Sam Lewis, Music by Ray Henderson

To help you imagine how your performance of this tune should sound, picture a scene from the 'Roaring Twenties'; fashionable young ladies with long strings of beads dancing the Charleston! Composer Ray Henderson, who also co-wrote 'Bye Bye Blackbird' and 'Don't Bring Lulu', was a pianist in dance bands and vaudeville, as well as being a church organist.

Make your performance bouncy and full of energy, the piece is quite fast and needs a lively beat – it's a two in a bar feel, counting in minims rather than crotchets. Play separate bows staccato and keep aiming for the first beat of each bar, where a slight accent will help maintain the pulse. To avoid lots of open strings use the suggested fingering. This involves more 'fiddle style' string crossing, which sounds a bit jazzier!

© 1925 & 1996 EMI Catalogue Partnership and EMI Feist Catalog Inc, USA
Worldwide print rights controlled by Warner Bros Publications Inc/IMP Ltd
Anglo Pic Music Co Ltd, London WC2H 8NA and Redwood Music Ltd, London NW1 8BD

Satin doll

Words and Music by Billy Strayhorn, Duke Ellington and Johnny Mercer

Duke Ellington was a composer and arranger of enormous output, always working wherever he was. He toured constantly and wrote music in airport lounges and in the backs of cars. Once, when he ran out of paper, he sketched out an idea on the cuff of his shirt sleeve! Co-writer Billy Strayhorn worked with Ellington for a long time. He wrote 'Take The A-Train' which became known as the Ellington band's theme tune.

Play this piece with a warm sound; using some vibrato will help. It needs a long, gentle feel. Keep the pulse steady and avoid making any accents with the bow. The rhythm may look more complicated than it is to play. In bar 4, for instance, imagine the first beat is struck by someone else and you catch the off beat.

© 1953, 1960 & 1996 Tempo Music Inc, USA
Campbell Connelly & Co Ltd, London W1V 5TZ

Jumpin' at the woodside

Words by Jon Hendricks, Music by Count Basie

This tune appeared on the album of the same name, recorded by Count Basie and his orchestra in the late 1930s. Count Basie was a career jazz pianist and band leader who, in his early years, took informal guidance in 'stride' piano from the showman and songwriter, Fats Waller. Working with Basie in what became one of the greatest 'swing' outfits ever were such jazz masters as Lester Young (tenor saxophone), Buck Clayton (trumpet), Earl Warren (alto saxophone) and Herschel Evans (clarinet).

This one is a bit of a finger-twister, co-ordination between hands could be a problem. Practise slowly at first and resist the temptation to increase the tempo before you are absolutely sure where everything is. You might find it is comfortable to play the whole piece in third position, except for the very last note. For the opening section use a fast up bow and save your bow through the long tied notes.

© 1938 & 1996 Bregman Vocco & Conn Inc, USA

Warner/Chappell Music Ltd, London W1Y 3FA

Reproduced and printed by Halstan & Co. Ltd., Amersham, Bucks., England

Blue moon

Words by Lorenz Hart, Music by Richard Rodgers

© 1934 & 1996 EMI Catalogue Partnership and EMI Robbins Catalog Inc, USA
Worldwide print rights controlled by Warner Bros Publications Inc/IMP Ltd

18

Five foot two, eyes of blue
(Has anybody seen my girl?)

Words by Joe Young and Sam Lewis, Music by Ray Henderson

© 1925 & 1996 EMI Catalogue Partnership sand EMI Feist Catalog Inc, USA
Worldwide print rights controlled by Warner Bros Publications Inc/IMP Ltd
Anglo Pic Music Co Ltd, London WC2H 8NA and Redwood Music Ltd, London NW1 8BD

Satin doll

Words and Music by Billy Strayhorn, Duke Ellington and Johnny Mercer

© 1953, 1960 & 1996 Tempo Music Inc, USA

Campbell Connelly & Co Ltd, London W1V 5TZ

Jumpin' at the woodside

Words by Jon Hendricks, Music by Count Basie

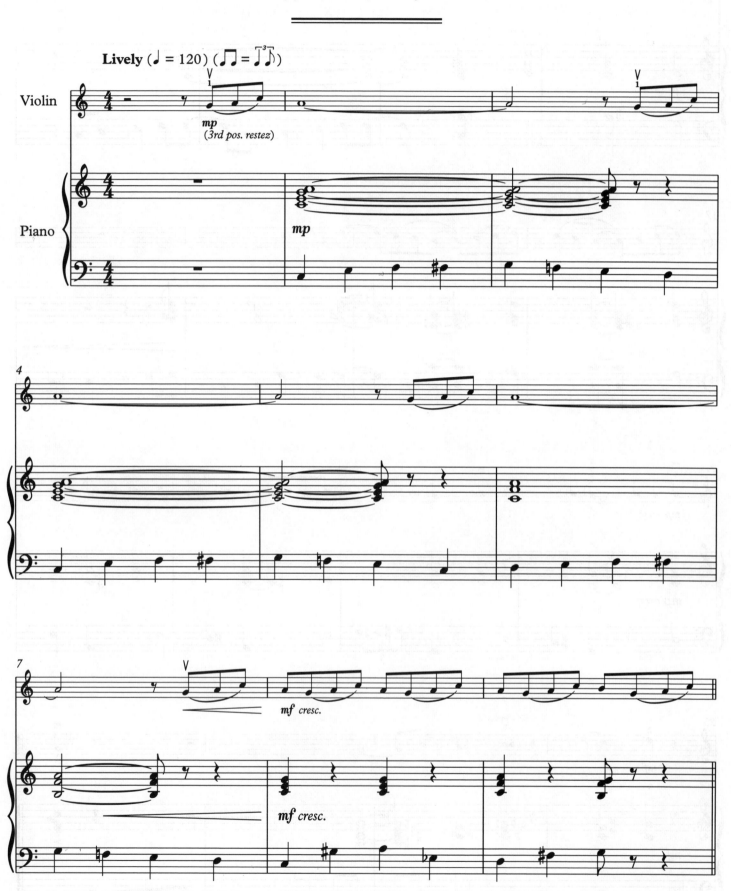

© 1938 & 1996 Bregman Vocco & Conn Inc, USA
Warner/Chappell Music Ltd, London W1Y 3FA

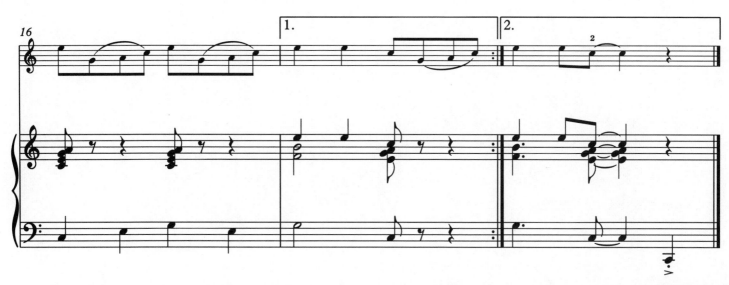

Reproduced and printed by
Halstan & Co. Ltd., Amersham, Bucks., England